Contents

Links to Abacus weekly plans

This information is for teachers who want to see how the Mastery Checkpoints are planned into the Abacus maths programme.

Autumn term 1		
Week 1	Checkpoint 1	Using number facts to add and subtract
Week 3	Checkpoint 2	Doubling and halving
Week 4	Checkpoint 3	3D shapes
Week 5	Checkpoint 4	Place value in 3-digit numbers
Autumn term 2		
Week 6	Checkpoint 5	Fractions
Week 6	Checkpoint 6	Finding fractions of amounts
Week 7	Checkpoint 7	Place value in money
Week 7	Checkpoint 8	Adding to the next 10 or to 100
Week 8	Checkpoint 9	Length and capacity
Week 10	Checkpoint 10	The 2, 3, 4, 5 and 10 times-tables
Spring term 1		
Week 11	Checkpoint 11	1, 10 and 100 more and less, and counting in 10s, 50s and 100s
Week 12	Checkpoint 12	Doubling, halving, multiplying by 4 and finding a quarter
Week 13	Checkpoint 13	Equivalent fractions
Week 14	Checkpoint 14	2D shapes
Week 14	Checkpoint 15	Right angles and turns
Week 15	Checkpoint 16	Placing numbers on lines and rounding
Week 15	Checkpoint 17	Using counting up on a number line to subtract and find change
Spring term 2		
Week 17	Checkpoint 18	Mental and written addition
Week 18	Checkpoint 19	Telling the time
Week 19	Checkpoint 20	Ordering numbers up to 1000
Week 20	Checkpoint 21	Using the grid method
Summer term 1		
Week 21	Checkpoint 22	Adding and subtracting 1s, 10s and 100s to and from 3-digit numbers
Week 21	Checkpoint 23	Adding, subtracting and comparing fractions
Week 22	Checkpoint 24	The 2, 3, 4, 5, 8 and 10 times-tables
Week 23	Checkpoint 25	Division
Week 24	Checkpoint 26	Weight
Week 24	Checkpoint 27	Tables, pictograms and bar charts
Summer term 2		
Week 27	Checkpoint 28	Subtraction by counting up
Week 28	Checkpoint 29	Finding perimeters
Week 28	Checkpoint 30	Telling the time
Week 29	Checkpoint 31	Multiplication and division
Week 29	Checkpoint 32	Tenths
Week 30	Checkpoint 33	Mental and written addition
Week 30	Checkpoint 34	Adding and subtracting money

How to use this book

Mastery Checkpoints

The Mastery Checkpoints give you a chance to show how much you have learned about a key maths skill, straight after you have learned about it in lessons.

Each Checkpoint starts with a few questions for everyone to try. These are followed by some more in-depth questions in the Champions' Challenge section.

The title tells you which skill the Checkpoint is about.

Read each question carefully!

The Champions' Challenge section gives you more challenging questions.

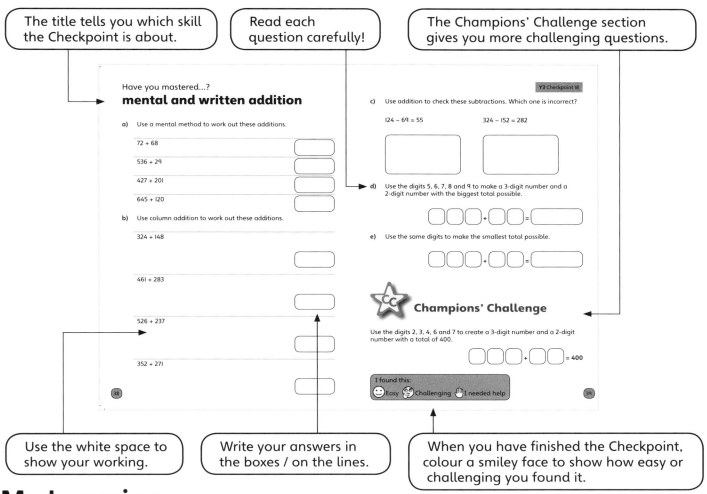

Use the white space to show your working.

Write your answers in the boxes / on the lines.

When you have finished the Checkpoint, colour a smiley face to show how easy or challenging you found it.

My Learning

On pages 74–79 you will find opportunities for you to reflect on your own learning: for example, how you and your classmates have helped each other to learn, what important questions you have asked, and what connections you have found between different areas of maths. Your teacher will tell you when to complete each of these pages.

My Mastery

On pages 80–85 you will find tables that list the Checkpoint skills, and give you a chance to re-assess how confident you feel about each of them later in the year. Your teacher will tell you when to complete these self-assessments, for example at the end of each half-term.

Have you mastered...?
using number facts to add and subtract

Use your knowledge of number facts to help you to answer these questions.

a) $4 + 8 + 12 =$ ☐

  $7 + 5 + 7 =$ ☐

  $6 + 8 + 4 =$ ☐

  $4 + 8 + 8 =$ ☐

b) $73 + 4 =$ ☐

  $88 - 3 =$ ☐

  $36 + 7 =$ ☐

  $63 - 5 =$ ☐

c)   Write digits in the boxes to make three pairs of numbers, each with a total of 100.

☐ 5 + ☐ 5 = 100   ☐ 5 + ☐ 5 = 100

☐ 5 + ☐ 5 = 100

Champions' Challenge

I)   948 – 5 = ⬚

589 + 3 = ⬚

637 + 4 = ⬚

722 – 3 = ⬚

2)   Adding 7 to any number ending in 5, always gives a number ending in:

3)   Write three trios of single-digit numbers, each with a total of I6.

⬚ + ⬚ + ⬚ = I6

⬚ + ⬚ + ⬚ = I6

⬚ + ⬚ + ⬚ = I6

I found this:
☺ Easy   🤔 Challenging   ✋ I needed help

Have you mastered...?
doubling and halving

a) Double 16 is [   ]   Half of 24 is [   ]

Double [   ] is 28   Half of [   ] is 20

b) Draw lines to match the numbers to their doubles:

15	68
22	94
34	30
47	44

c) These t-shirts and hoodies are half price! Write the new prices.

£18   £22   £34   £56

[   ] [   ] [   ] [   ]

Champions' Challenge

1)   Ben started with a number less than 10 to make a doubling chain. Fill in the missing numbers.

[   ] , [   ] , [   ] , 56, 112

2)   Pearl started her doubling chain with the number 7.
Will her chain include any other odd numbers? Why/why not?

_____

_____

3)   Hassan doubled a number less than 10 four times. 128 was the last number he wrote. What number did he start with?

[   ]

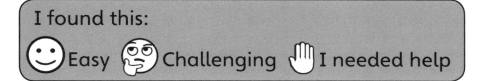

Have you mastered...?

3D shapes

a) Write **always**, **sometimes** or **never** for each statement.

Cuboids have six flat faces. _____

Pyramids have a square base. _____

Cones have two corners (vertices). _____

Spheres have no corners (vertices). _____

b) Draw and name a shape with six square faces.

_____

c) Draw and name a shape with two flat faces and one curved face. The two flat faces are circles of the same size.

_____

Champions' Challenge

Kyle made two cylinders out of modelling dough.

He cuts one vertically through the middle, and the other horizontally across the middle.

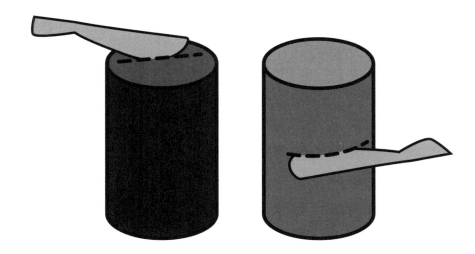

He looks at the pair of new surfaces each time. What shapes are they?

_____

_____

_____

_____

_____

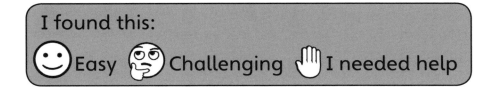

9

Have you mastered...?

place value in 3-digit numbers

a) Find the missing numbers.

200 + 40 + 9 = ☐ ☐ ☐

800 + ☐ + 3 = 8 2 3

☐ + 60 + 1 = 7 6 1

b) Write these two numbers in the place value chart.

four hundred and two
six hundred and fifty

100s	10s	1s

c) Write a number where the digit 5 is worth 50.

d) Write a number where the digit 7 is worth 700.

Champions' Challenge

Esme says there are ten numbers between 100 and 200 which have one zero. How many do you think there are? Convince your teacher!

_____

_____

_____

_____

 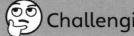
11

Have you mastered...?
fractions

a)   What fraction of each flag is shaded grey?

b)   Write < or > between each pair of fractions.

$\dfrac{1}{2}$ $\bigcirc$ $\dfrac{1}{4}$

$\dfrac{1}{6}$ $\bigcirc$ $\dfrac{1}{2}$

$\dfrac{1}{4}$ $\bigcirc$ $\dfrac{1}{6}$

Champions' Challenge

Write two fractions which are bigger than $\frac{1}{5}$ but smaller than $\frac{1}{2}$.

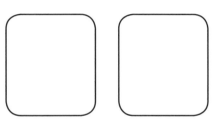

Can you write a fraction between $\frac{1}{2}$ and $\frac{3}{4}$?

finding fractions of amounts

Work out how many parsnips, cabbages and carrots are eaten by each rabbit.

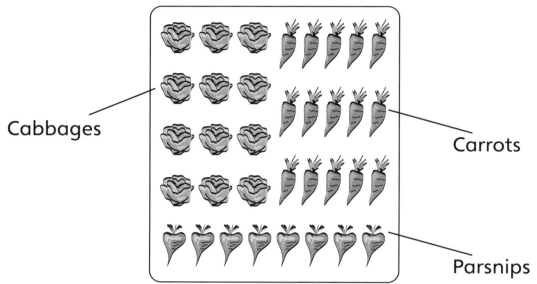

Cabbages

Carrots

Parsnips

a) Russ the rabbit eats $\frac{1}{4}$ of the parsnips and Ruth the rabbit eats $\frac{3}{4}$ of them.

Russ eats [   ] parsnips. Ruth eats [   ] parsnips.

b) Russ eats $\frac{1}{3}$ of the cabbages and Ruth eats $\frac{1}{4}$ of them.

Russ eats [   ] cabbages. Ruth eats [   ] cabbages.

c) Russ eats $\frac{2}{3}$ of the carrots and Ruth eats $\frac{1}{5}$ of them.

Russ eats [   ] carrots. Ruth eats [   ] carrots.

Champions' Challenge

1) How many cabbages are left?

What fraction of the cabbages is this?

2) Russ eats $\frac{2}{5}$ of the turnips, and Ruth eats $\frac{1}{5}$ of the turnips.

There are 4 turnips left. How many were there to start with?

15

Have you mastered...?
place value in money

a)

59p + 30p = ☐

£2 + 30p + 5p = ☐

£5·09 + 70p = ☐

£1·20 + 5p = ☐

b)

75p − 20p = ☐

£2·75 − 70p = ☐

£6·35 − 5p = ☐

£1 − 1p = ☐

c) Sketch a combination of coins that make £2·57.

Champions' Challenge

1) What is the smallest number of coins you can use to pay £3·75? Which coins are they?

_____

_____

2) Show how to pay £3·75 using eight coins.

_____

_____

I found this:

😊 Easy 🤔 Challenging ✋ I needed help

Have you mastered...?
adding to the next 10 or to 100

a) 37 + ⬚ = 40

   52 + ⬚ = 60

   ⬚ + 5 = 30

   ⬚ + 6 = 90

b) 68 + ⬚ = 100

   73 + ⬚ = 100

   ⬚ + 15 = 100

   ⬚ + 34 = 100

c) When finding a pair of numbers with a total of 100, the 10s always add up to ⬚ and the 1s always add up to ⬚.
(Except when adding two multiples of 10!)

Champions' Challenge

1) Find two even numbers with a total of 100.

$$\boxed{} + \boxed{} = 100$$

2) Find two odd numbers with a total of 100.

$$\boxed{} + \boxed{} = 100$$

3) Can you find an odd number and an even number with a total of 100? *Hint: think about the 1s digits total.*

_____

_____

_____

I found this:

 Easy  Challenging ✋ I needed help

Have you mastered...?
length and capacity

a) Draw a line exactly 10 cm long.

b) Circle the most likely length for each creature.

A hedgehog is   2 cm long   20 cm long   2 metres long

A spider is   3 cm long   30 cm long   3 metres long

An elephant is   6 cm long   60 cm long   6 metres long

c) Write < or > between 500 ml and 2 litres.

500 ml $\bigcirc$ 2 litres

d) Which of these statements is incorrect?

A: a bucket holds 8 litres

B: a teaspoon holds 5 litres

C: a mug holds 300 ml

Champions' Challenge

1) A mouse is 10 cm long. How many mice are the same length as a 2-metre tiger?

2) A cup holds 250 ml. How many cups of water would it take to fill a 2-litre bottle?

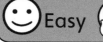 I found this:

 Easy 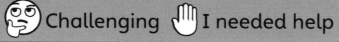 Challenging 🖐 I needed help

Have you mastered...?

the 2, 3, 4, 5 and 10 times-tables

a) $5 \times 4 = \boxed{}$ $8 \times 4 = \boxed{}$ $7 \times 3 = \boxed{}$

b) $\boxed{} \times 5 = 30$ $\boxed{} \times 3 = 27$ $\boxed{} \times 2 = 14$

c) $50 \div 10 = \boxed{}$ $22 \div 2 = \boxed{}$ $16 \div 4 = \boxed{}$

d)   Write two multiplications and two divisions to go with the picture of stars.

$\boxed{}$ $\boxed{}$

$\boxed{}$ $\boxed{}$

e) Write as many different multiplications as you can with an answer of 30.

 # Champions' Challenge

l) Write four divisions with an answer of 4.

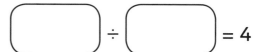

$\boxed{} \div \boxed{} = 4$

$\boxed{} \div \boxed{} = 4$

$\boxed{} \div \boxed{} = 4$

$\boxed{} \div \boxed{} = 4$

I found this:
 Easy 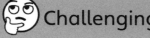 Challenging 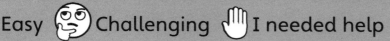 I needed help

Have you mastered...?

I, 10 and 100 more and less, and counting in 10s, 50s and 100s

a) Find 1 more than each number.   238   600   499

b) Find 10 less than each number.   365   212   405

c) Find 100 less than each number.   437   690   132

d) Write the next three numbers in each sequence.

265   275   285

75   125   175

308   408   508

Champions' Challenge

1) Think of a number you will say in each count if you start on 125 and count in steps of 10, 50 and 100.

2) Think of a number you will say if you start at 125 and count in steps of 10 and 50, but that you won't say if you count in steps of 100.

I found this:

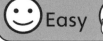Easy Challenging I needed help

25

Have you mastered...?
doubling, halving, multiplying by 4 and finding a quarter

a) Which number will come out of this function machine?

24 → [double] → [halve] → ⬭

b) Which numbers will come out of these function machines? For each one, draw a machine with just one function that will do the same job.

16 → [double] → [double] → ⬭

⬭

48 → [halve] → [halve] → ⬭

⬭

c) Multiply these numbers by 4.

23 ⬭

17 ⬭

36 ⬭

d) Find $\frac{1}{4}$ of these numbers.

28

84

52

Champions' Challenge

Which number will come out of, or went into, these function machines? For each one, draw a machine with just one function that will do the same job.

24 → double → halve → double →

→ double → double → double → 104

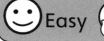 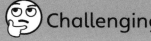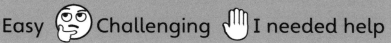

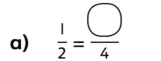

Have you mastered...?
equivalent fractions

a) $\dfrac{1}{2} = \dfrac{\bigcirc}{4}$

$\dfrac{\bigcirc}{2} = \dfrac{4}{8}$

$\dfrac{3}{4} = \dfrac{\bigcirc}{8}$

1			
$\frac{1}{2}$		$\frac{1}{2}$	
$\frac{1}{4}$	$\frac{1}{4}$	$\frac{1}{4}$	$\frac{1}{4}$
$\frac{1}{8}$ $\frac{1}{8}$	$\frac{1}{8}$ $\frac{1}{8}$	$\frac{1}{8}$ $\frac{1}{8}$	$\frac{1}{8}$ $\frac{1}{8}$

b) $\dfrac{1}{2} = \dfrac{\bigcirc}{6}$

$\dfrac{\bigcirc}{3} = \dfrac{2}{6}$

$\dfrac{2}{3} = \dfrac{\bigcirc}{6}$

1		
$\frac{1}{2}$		$\frac{1}{2}$
$\frac{1}{3}$	$\frac{1}{3}$	$\frac{1}{3}$
$\frac{1}{6}$ $\frac{1}{6}$	$\frac{1}{6}$ $\frac{1}{6}$	$\frac{1}{6}$ $\frac{1}{6}$

c) Sketch a line from 0 to 1. Mark $\dfrac{1}{4}$ and $\dfrac{3}{4}$ on it.

d) Sketch a new line from 0 to 1. Mark $\dfrac{1}{3}$ and $\dfrac{2}{3}$ on it.

e) Sketch a new line from 0 to 1. Mark $\dfrac{4}{8}$ and $\dfrac{7}{8}$ on it.

Champions' Challenge

Write five fractions that are equivalent to $\frac{1}{2}$.

None of them should already have been used on this Checkpoint!

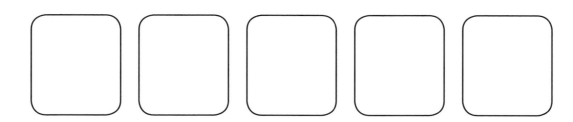

Write two fractions that are equivalent to $\frac{1}{4}$.

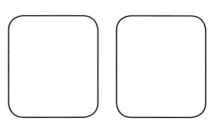

I found this:

 Easy Challenging ✋ I needed help

29

Have you mastered...?
2D shapes

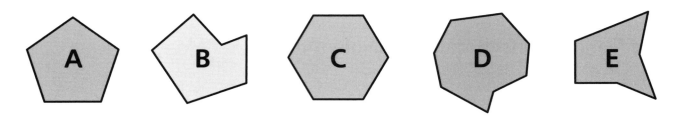

a) Write the letters of all the hexagons.

_____

b) Draw a pentagon with sides of different lengths.

c) Write **true** or **false** for each statement.

A quadrilateral has four straight sides.

_____

Only squares and rectangles have right angles.

_____

A quadrilateral can have an angle of more than 180°.

_____

Champions' Challenge

1) Draw a pentagon with two right angles.

2) Draw a hexagon with two right angles.

3) Draw a quadrilateral with only two right angles.

I found this:

Easy Challenging ✋I needed help

31

Have you mastered...?
right angles and turns

a) Write the letters of:

the right angles

_____

the angle that is less than 90°

_____

the angles that are more than 90°.

_____

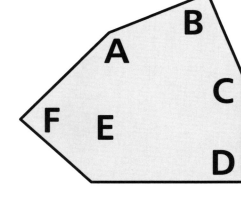

b) Which letter will the needle be on if:

it spins 90°clockwise?

_____

it spins 360°?

_____

it spins $\frac{3}{4}$ of a full turn clockwise?

_____

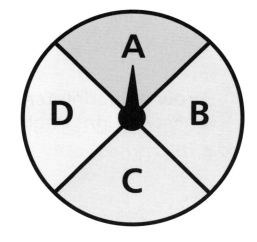

Champions' Challenge

Write **true** or **false** for each statement.

There are six right angles in a full turn.

_____

Half of a right angle is 45°.

_____

Half of a full turn is 200°.

_____

$\frac{3}{4}$ of a full turn is 270°.

_____

I found this:
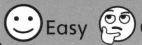 Easy Challenging 🖐 I needed help

33

Have you mastered...?

placing numbers on lines and rounding

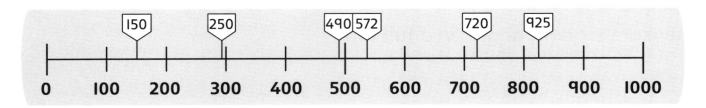

a) Which tags are wrong? Estimate which numbers should have been written on the tags.

_____

_____

_____

b) Sketch a line from 400 to 500. Mark on the numbers 449, 425 and 491.

c) Round each number on your line to the nearest 100 and to the nearest 10.

449   nearest 100 [   ]   nearest 10 [   ]

425   nearest 100 [   ]   nearest 10 [   ]

491   nearest 100 [   ]   nearest 10 [   ]

Champions' Challenge

1)   Think of a number that rounds up to 250 when rounded to the nearest 10 but rounds down to 200 when rounded to the nearest 100.

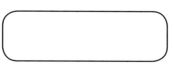

2)   Think of a number that rounds down to 250 when rounded to the nearest 10 but rounds up to 300 when rounded to the nearest 100.

I found this:

 Easy 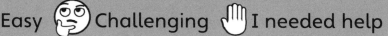 Challenging   I needed help

Have you mastered...?
using counting up on a number line to subtract and find change

a) Use counting up on a number line to work out these subtractions.

105 – 78

114 – 96

125 – 86

A £4·70
£6·75 B
£3·50 C
D £2·85
E £7·20
£8·45 F

b) Which of these soft toys could you buy with £5? Work out what change you would get for each.

Toy ⬜ ⬜

Toy ⬜ ⬜

Toy ⬜ ⬜

c) Work out the change from £10 for the other three soft toys.

Toy ⬚ ⬚

Toy ⬚ ⬚

Toy ⬚ ⬚

⭐ Champions' Challenge

1) 135 – 87 = 48. Write two other subtractions with the same answer. One number must be more than 100.

2) Eva bought a soft toy and got £1·75 change from £5. How much did her toy cost?

⬚

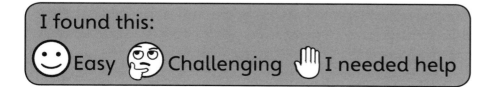

I found this:
☺ Easy   🤔 Challenging   ✋ I needed help

37

Have you mastered...?
mental and written addition

a) Use a mental method to work out these additions.

72 + 68

536 + 29

427 + 201

645 + 120

b) Use column addition to work out these additions.

324 + 148

461 + 283

526 + 237

352 + 271

c) Use addition to check these subtractions. Which one is incorrect?

124 – 69 = 55   324 – 152 = 282

d) Use the digits 5, 6, 7, 8 and 9 to make a 3-digit number and a 2-digit number with the biggest total possible.

e) Use the same digits to make the smallest total possible.

⬜⬜⬜ + ⬜⬜ = ⬜

 **Champions' Challenge**

Use the digits 2, 3, 4, 6 and 7 to create a 3-digit number and a 2-digit number with a total of 400.

 = 400

I found this:

 Easy   Challenging 🤚 I needed help

39

Have you mastered...?
telling the time

a) Write each time in words.

_____

_____

_____

b) Bradley leaves home at 8:35, and arrives at school at 8:50. He leaves school at 3:20 and arrives home at 3:40.

Which is quicker, his journey to school or his journey home?

_____

_____

c) Bradley writes out the 4 times-table in 120 seconds. Jess writes the 4 times-table in one minute and 30 seconds. Who is quicker?

_____

Champions' Challenge

1) Bradley takes 120 seconds to write each times-table. How many minutes would it take him to write all the times-tables from the 1 times-table to the 12 times-table?

2) If Jess takes one minute and 30 seconds to write each times-table, how many minutes would it take her to write all the times-tables from the 1 times-table to the 12 times-table?

I found this:

  Easy 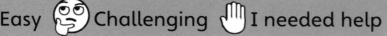 Challenging I needed help

Have you mastered...?
ordering numbers up to 1000

a) Write < or > between each pair of numbers.

325 ⬚ 253   467 ⬚ 476   801 ⬚ 765

b) Think of five numbers between 500 and 600. Write them in order, smallest first.

⬚

⬚

⬚

⬚

⬚

c) Use the digits 3, 4 and 5 to write a number between 350 and 450.

⬚

d) Use the digits 3, 4 and 5 to write a number between 450 and 550.

⬚

Champions' Challenge

Write the digits 1 to 5 in these numbers so that the numbers are in order from smallest to largest. You can only use each digit once.

☐ 6 4

1 6 ☐

3 ☐ 3

3 3 ☐

☐ 1 6

 I found this:
😊 Easy  🤔 Challenging ✋ I needed help

43

Have you mastered...?
using the grid method

4 × 13   4 × 10   4 × 3

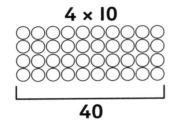

40   12

a) Use the grid method to work out these multiplications.

4 × 13

3 × 15

5 × 18

6 × 14

3 × 24

23 × 4

8 × 21

22 × 5

b) 4 × 12 = 48. Write two different multiplications which have double this answer.

Champions' Challenge

Write the 24 times-table up to 10 × 24!

Hint: You do not need to use the grid method for every multiplication. Think how you can use some of the smaller answers to help you work out the larger ones.

1 × 24 =

2 × 24 =

3 × 24 =

4 × 24 =

5 × 24 =

6 × 24 =

7 × 24 =

8 × 24 =

9 × 24 =

10 × 24 =

I found this:

Easy Challenging I needed help

45

adding and subtracting Is, I0s and I00s to and from 3-digit numbers

a) Solve these additions and subtractions.

437 + 5 = [ ]

634 + 40 = [ ]

578 + 30 = [ ]

437 + 500 = [ ]

757 − 40 = [ ]

983 − 60 = [ ]

821 − 40 = [ ]

983 − 600 = [ ]

478 + [ ] = 483

478 + [ ] = 699

478 + [ ] = 878

b) Add I20 to:

436 [ ]

285 [ ]

869 [ ]

208 [ ]

122 [ ]

c) Complete this number sentence.

[ ] + 134 = 123 + 40

Champions' Challenge

Think of three different fact families.

> *For example:*
> Fact family: **7, 5 and 12**
>
> *(7 + 5 = 12, 12 − 5 = 7, 12 − 7 = 5)*

Then write five additions or subtractions using each family. They must all involve a 3-digit number and a 1-digit number.

> For example:
> **127 + 5 = 132**
> **647 + 5 = 652**
> **342 − 5 = 337**
> **172 − 5 = 167**
> **987 + 5 = 992**

Fact families:

Additions and subtractions:

_____   _____   _____

_____   _____   _____

_____   _____   _____

_____   _____   _____

_____   _____   _____

I found this:
☺ Easy   🤔 Challenging   ✋ I needed help

Have you mastered...?

adding, subtracting and comparing fractions

a) Write >, < or = between each pair of fractions.

$\frac{3}{7}$ ⬚ $\frac{1}{7}$ $\frac{5}{8}$ ⬚ $\frac{3}{8}$ $\frac{2}{5}$ ⬚ $\frac{4}{5}$

$\frac{1}{2}$ ⬚ $\frac{4}{8}$ $\frac{1}{2}$ ⬚ $\frac{3}{4}$ $\frac{1}{2}$ ⬚ $\frac{1}{10}$

b) Write four fractions that are equal to $\frac{1}{2}$.

⬚ ⬚ ⬚ ⬚

c) Solve these additions and subtractions.

$\frac{5}{8} + \frac{2}{8}$ ⬚ $\frac{3}{5} + \frac{2}{5}$ ⬚

$\frac{6}{7} - \frac{2}{7}$ ⬚ $\frac{9}{10} - \frac{4}{10}$ ⬚

d) Fill in the missing numbers.

$\frac{5}{6} + \frac{\boxed{}}{6} = 1$ $\frac{5}{8} + \frac{\boxed{}}{8} = 1$ $1 - \frac{1}{3} = \boxed{}$

 # Champions' Challenge

1) Write at least four fractions that are less than $\frac{1}{2}$.

2) Write at least four fractions that are more than $\frac{1}{2}$.

I found this:
 Easy Challenging ✋ I needed help

Have you mastered...?
the 2, 3, 4, 5, 8 and 10 times-tables

a) Solve these multiplications and divisions.

$9 \times 3 = \boxed{}$

$6 \times 8 = \boxed{}$

$8 \times 4 = \boxed{}$

$\boxed{} \times 5 = 45$

$\boxed{} \times 4 = 28$

$\boxed{} \times 8 = 24$

$55 \div 5 = \boxed{}$

$18 \div 2 = \boxed{}$

$80 \div 8 = \boxed{}$

b) Write two multiplications and two divisions using the numbers 3, 8 and 24.

c) Write as many different multiplications as you can with an answer of 40.

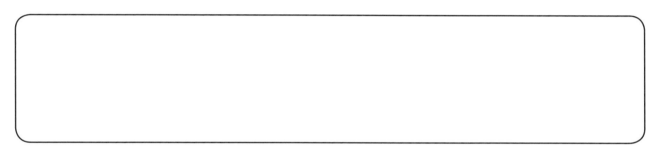

Champions' Challenge

Work out the missing numbers.

1) $\boxed{} \times 2 \times 3 = 24$

2) $5 \times \boxed{} = 50 \div 2$

3) $4 \times 3 = 48 \div \boxed{}$

I found this:

 Easy Challenging 🤚 I needed help

Have you mastered...?
division

a) Find the missing numbers. You can sketch number line jottings if it helps.

$$\boxed{} \times 5 = 75$$

$$\boxed{} \times 4 = 56$$

$$\boxed{} \times 3 = 48$$

b) Solve these divisions.

$$52 \div 4 = \boxed{}$$

$$42 \div 3 = \boxed{}$$

$$63 \div 5 = \boxed{} \; r \; \boxed{}$$

$$57 \div 4 = \boxed{} \; r \; \boxed{}$$

c) Apples are put into packs of 4.

How many apples will be left over if there are:

50 apples?

59 apples?

Champions' Challenge

Write numbers in each division to make it true.

$$\boxed{} \div 5 = \boxed{} \text{ r } 1$$

$$\boxed{} \div 5 = \boxed{} \text{ r } 2$$

$$\boxed{} \div 5 = \boxed{} \text{ r } 3$$

$$\boxed{} \div 5 = \boxed{} \text{ r } 4$$

I found this:

 Easy Challenging I needed help

Have you mastered...?
weight

a) Which of the objects might weigh these weights?

1 gram _____

200 grams _____

500 grams _____

1000 grams _____

4 kilograms _____

b) Write the name of an object that is heavier than any of these objects.

_____

c) Write the name of a different object that might weigh between 1 gram and 1 kilogram.

_____

Champions' Challenge

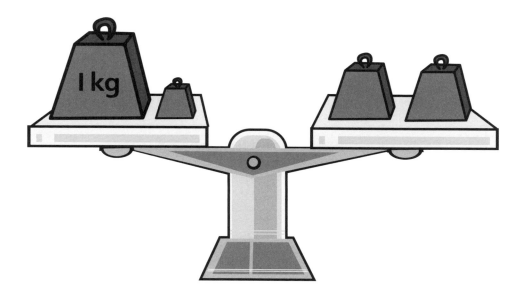

There are three mystery weights on these balances. Two are identical.
Write a possible number of grams for each weight.

_____

_____

_____

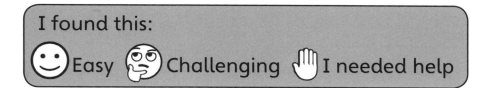

I found this:

😊 Easy 🤔 Challenging ✋ I needed help

55

Have you mastered...?
tables, pictograms and bar charts

Each child in Class 1 voted for their favourite type of film.
Look at this table, which shows the results.

Favourite types of film in Class 1

Type of film	Number of votes
Animal	10
Mystery	3
Comedy	8
Magic	6

a) Draw a pictogram to show the results, where 1 symbol stands for 2 children.

Use the grid opposite.

b) How many more children prefer films about animals to mystery films?

c) How many children are in Class 1?

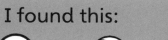 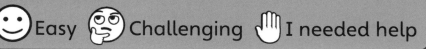

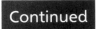

tables, pictograms and bar charts

Each child in Class 2 voted for their favourite type of film.

Look at this bar chart, which shows the results.

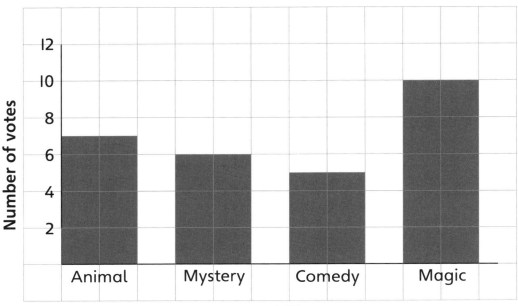

Favourite types of film in Class 2

d) How many more children prefer films about mystery to comedy films?

e) How many children are in Class 2?

Champions' Challenge

Favourite types of film in Class 1

Type of film	Number of votes
Animal	10
Mystery	3
Comedy	8
Magic	6

1)   How many more children in Class 2 prefer films about magic than children in Class 1?

2)   How many fewer children in Class 2 prefer comedy films than children in Class 1?

I found this:

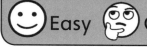 Easy Challenging ✋ I needed help

Have you mastered...?
subtraction by counting up

a) Draw number line jottings to work out these subtractions:

876 – 789

765 – 678

654 – 567

543 – 456

432 – 345

321 – 234

210 – 123

b) What do you notice about your answers?

_____

_____

c) Jimmy scored 867 on a computer game yesterday. Today he scored 937! What is the difference between his two scores?

Champions' Challenge

1) Fill in the boxes to write two subtractions with an answer of less than 50. You may not use a digit twice within each subtraction!

$$4\boxed{}\boxed{} - 3\boxed{}\boxed{}$$

$$4\boxed{}\boxed{} - 3\boxed{}\boxed{}$$

2) Write two more subtractions with an answer of more than 50.

$$4\boxed{}\boxed{} - 3\boxed{}\boxed{}$$

$$4\boxed{}\boxed{} - 3\boxed{}\boxed{}$$

I found this:

☺ Easy 🤔 Challenging ✋ I needed help

finding perimeters

a) Draw three squares: one with sides of 5 cm, one with sides of 6 cm and one with sides of 7 cm. Find the perimeter of each square.

b) Draw two rectangles; one that is 4 cm by 3 cm and one that is 6 cm by 4 cm. Find the perimeter of each rectangle.

c) Draw your own pentagon and find its perimeter to the nearest centimetre.

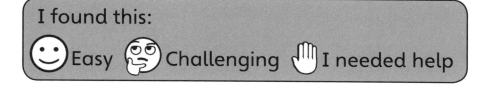 Champions' Challenge

Draw two different shapes with a perimeter of 20 cm.

I found this:

☺ Easy   🤔 Challenging   ✋ I needed help

63

Have you mastered...?
telling the time

a) Write whether the times shown are in the morning, afternoon, evening or night. Say if any are noon or midnight.

3:15 pm _____

8:30 am _____

7:45 pm _____

 _____

 _____

b) How many minutes before or after 6 o'clock does each clock show? Circle the clock that shows the time closest to 6 o'clock.

_____

_____

_____

c) Write these lengths of time in order, shortest first.

2 hours   70 minutes   2 minutes   180 seconds

_____

_____

 # Champions' Challenge

This clock shows a time in the afternoon.

1) Write the time it shows in three different ways.

_____

_____

_____

2) Try writing the time as it would appear on a 24-hour clock.

I found this:

 Easy Challenging I needed help

Have you mastered...?
multiplication and division

a) Use the grid method to work out these multiplications.

3 × 34

⬭

5 × 48

⬭

4 × 36

⬭

b) Work out what numbers have been multiplied together in these grids.

×	40	3
?	200	15

 × 43 = 215

×	?	?
8	160	24

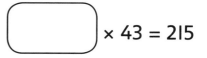

8 × ⬭ = 184

Use multiplication or division to work out the answers to these number stories.

c) Ali has 52 chairs in the café. She puts 4 chairs round each table. How many tables does she have?

d) Ali has 32 packs of 4 tea cakes. How many tea cakes is this?

Champions' Challenge

Work out the missing numbers in these divisions.

$\boxed{} \div 3 = 26$

$68 \div \boxed{} = 17$

Have you mastered...?
tenths

a) What fraction of each tray has eggs in it?

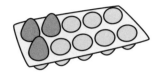 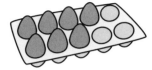 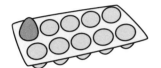 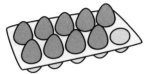

b) Solve these calculations.

$\frac{1}{10}$ of 40 is ⬚

$\frac{3}{10}$ of 40 is ⬚

$\frac{1}{10}$ of 400 is ⬚

$\frac{7}{10}$ of 400 is ⬚

$\frac{1}{10}$ of 140 is ⬚

$\frac{3}{10}$ of 140 is ⬚

$\frac{1}{10}$ of 240 is ⬚

$\frac{2}{10}$ of 240 is ⬚

$\frac{\bigcirc}{10}$ of 100 is 10

$\frac{\bigcirc}{10}$ of 100 is 30

Champions' Challenge

Write these fractions as tenths. Draw a picture to prove to your teacher that you are right!

$\frac{1}{5}$ $\frac{2}{5}$ $\frac{3}{5}$ $\frac{4}{5}$ $\frac{1}{2}$

I found this:

 Easy   Challenging   ✋ I needed help

69

mental and written addition

a) Use a mental method to work out these additions.

240 + 350

534 + 210

420 + 200 + 140

b) Use column addition to work out these additions.

524 + 238

351 + 272

326 + 231 + 234

c) Choose a mental or written method to work out these additions.

456 + 218 + 127

450 + 210 + 100

 **Champions' Challenge**

Use the digits 1, 2, 3, 4, 5, 6, 7, 8 and 9 to make three 3-digit numbers that add together to make the smallest total possible.

◯ + ◯ + ◯ = ◯

Have you mastered...?
adding and subtracting money

£8·25
£4·30
£3·49
£5·45
£2·19
£7·85

It's summer!

a) Find the change from £10 for each of these beach toys.

Beach ball

Cricket set

Racket and ball set

Bucket and spade set

Inflatable dolphin

Rubber ring

b) Choose two subtractions to check using addition.

Champions' Challenge

1) Which two items do you think you could buy for a total of less than £10? Find the exact total and the change from £10.

$$\boxed{} + \boxed{} = \boxed{}$$

Change $\boxed{}$

2) Can you buy three items for less than £10?

_____

_____

 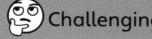

Date: _____

Thoughts on my learning

As we learn about a new topic in maths, we do lots of thinking! As you are working through a topic, stop and spend some time thinking about what you are learning.

Record some of your thoughts below. Use these sentence starters to help you.

I know… because

I think… because

I know… so I also know

I agree with… because

I disagree with… because

I wonder if…

Date: _____

Learning from each other

Did you know that we can learn a lot from each other? Together, you and your classmates can help each other understand maths by discussing and explaining ideas.

Think about how your classmates have helped you in your maths learning and how you have helped them.

How have you helped your classmates?

How have your classmates helped you?

Date: _____

Maths connections

Many of the different areas of maths overlap with each other. For example, if you are finding change from £5, this involves your skills and knowledge in subtraction, decimals, place value and measures.

What connections have you spotted between different areas of maths? What did you notice about them?

Date: _____

Asking questions

You might have heard of the phrase "there is no such thing as a silly question". This is definitely true when it comes to maths! Asking questions is a really important skill.

Think about the different questions you have asked during your maths learning. Why were these questions important?

Questions I have asked	Why they were important

Date: _____

My methods

There are lots of different ways to explain maths. You can use different methods and strategies to work out an answer and to help explain your understanding.

Choose one area of maths that you have been learning about. Record some of the different methods you used during your learning.

Date: _____

Reflection

At the end of a topic, stop and reflect on what you have learnt.

What do you understand now that you did not before?

What have you got better at? How do you know?

What is the most interesting thing you found out? Give an example.

Is there anything else about this topic you would like to find out more about?

Colour a circle for each skill to show how you feel about it now.

Mastery Checkpoint	Have you mastered...?	More help!	I think I'm OK	I'm the master!	Date
Checkpoint 1 pages 4–5	Using number facts to add and subtract	◯	◯	◯	
Checkpoint 2 pages 6–7	Doubling and halving	◯	◯	◯	
Checkpoint 3 pages 8–9	3D shapes	◯	◯	◯	
Checkpoint 4 pages 10–11	Place value in 3-digit numbers	◯	◯	◯	
Checkpoint 5 pages 12–13	Fractions	◯	◯	◯	
Checkpoint 6 pages 14–15	Finding fractions of amounts	◯	◯	◯	

Colour a circle for each skill to show how you feel about it now.

Mastery Checkpoint	Have you mastered...?	More help!	I think I'm OK	I'm the master!	Date
Checkpoint 7 pages 16–17	Place value in money	◯	◯	◯	
Checkpoint 8 pages 18–19	Adding to the next 10 or to 100	◯	◯	◯	
Checkpoint 9 pages 20–21	Length and capacity	◯	◯	◯	
Checkpoint 10 pages 22–23	The 2, 3, 4, 5 and 10 times-tables	◯	◯	◯	
Checkpoint 11 pages 24–25	1, 10 and 100 more and less, and counting in 10s, 50s and 100s	◯	◯	◯	
Checkpoint 12 pages 26–27	Doubling, halving, multiplying by 4 and finding a quarter	◯	◯	◯	

My Mastery

Colour a circle for each skill to show how you feel about it now.

Mastery Checkpoint	Have you mastered...?	More help!	I think I'm OK	I'm the master!	Date
Checkpoint 13 pages 28–29	Equivalent fractions	◯	◯	◯	
Checkpoint 14 pages 30–31	2D shapes	◯	◯	◯	
Checkpoint 15 pages 32–33	Right angles and turns	◯	◯	◯	
Checkpoint 16 pages 34–35	Placing numbers on lines and rounding	◯	◯	◯	
Checkpoint 17 pages 36–37	Using counting up on a number line to subtract and find change	◯	◯	◯	
Checkpoint 18 pages 38–39	Mental and written addition	◯	◯	◯	

Colour a circle for each skill to show how you feel about it now.

Mastery Checkpoint	Have you mastered...?	More help!	I think I'm OK	I'm the master!	Date
Checkpoint 19 pages 40–41	Telling the time	○	○	○	
Checkpoint 20 pages 42–43	Ordering numbers up to 1000	○	○	○	
Checkpoint 21 pages 44–45	Using the grid method	○	○	○	
Checkpoint 22 pages 46–47	Adding and subtracting 1s, 10s and 100s to and from 3-digit numbers	○	○	○	
Checkpoint 23 pages 48–49	Adding, subtracting and comparing fractions	○	○	○	
Checkpoint 24 pages 50–51	The 2, 3, 4, 5, 8 and 10 times-tables	○	○	○	

Colour a circle for each skill to show how you feel about it now.

Mastery Checkpoint	Have you mastered...?	More help!	I think I'm OK	I'm the master!	Date
Checkpoint 25 pages 52–53	Division	◯	◯	◯	
Checkpoint 26 pages 54–55	Weight	◯	◯	◯	
Checkpoint 27 pages 56–59	Tables, pictograms and bar charts	◯	◯	◯	
Checkpoint 28 pages 60–61	Subtraction by counting up	◯	◯	◯	
Checkpoint 29 pages 62–63	Finding perimeters	◯	◯	◯	
Checkpoint 30 pages 64–65	Telling the time	◯	◯	◯	

Colour a circle for each skill to show how you feel about it now.

Mastery Checkpoint	Have you mastered...?	More help!	I think I'm OK	I'm the master!	Date
Checkpoint 31 pages 66–67	Multiplication and division	◯	◯	◯	
Checkpoint 32 pages 68–69	Tenths	◯	◯	◯	
Checkpoint 33 pages 70–71	Mental and written addition	◯	◯	◯	
Checkpoint 34 pages 72–73	Adding and subtracting money	◯	◯	◯	

Checkpoints ordered by curriculum domain

Number – number and place value		
Checkpoint 4	Place value in 3-digit numbers	10–11
Checkpoint 7*	Place value in money	16–17
Checkpoint 11	1, 10 and 100 more and less, and counting in 10s, 50s and 100s	24–25
Checkpoint 16	Placing numbers on lines and rounding	34–35
Checkpoint 20	Ordering numbers up to 1000	42–43
Number – addition and subtraction		
Checkpoint 1	Using number facts to add and subtract	4–5
Checkpoint 8	Adding to the next 10 or to 100	18–19
Checkpoint 17	Using counting up on a number line to subtract and find change	36–37
Checkpoint 18	Mental and written addition	38–39
Checkpoint 22	Adding and subtracting 1s, 10s and 100s to and from 3-digit numbers	46–47
Checkpoint 28	Subtraction by counting up	60–61
Checkpoint 33	Mental and written addition	70–71
Number – multiplication and division		
Checkpoint 2	Doubling and halving	6–7
Checkpoint 10	The 2, 3, 4, 5 and 10 times-tables	22–23
Checkpoint 12	Doubling, halving, multiplying by 4 and finding a quarter	26–27
Checkpoint 21	Using the grid method	44–45
Checkpoint 24	The 2, 3, 4, 5, 8 and 10 times-tables	50–51
Checkpoint 25	Division	52–53
Checkpoint 31	Multiplication and division	66–67
Number – fractions (including decimals and percentages)		
Checkpoint 5	Fractions	12–13
Checkpoint 6	Finding fractions of amounts	14–15
Checkpoint 13	Equivalent fractions	28–29
Checkpoint 23	Adding, subtracting and comparing fractions	48–49
Checkpoint 32	Tenths	68–69
Measurement		
Checkpoint 7*	Place value in money	16–17
Checkpoint 9	Length and capacity	20–21
Checkpoint 19	Telling the time	40–41
Checkpoint 26	Weight	54–55
Checkpoint 29	Finding perimeters	62–63
Checkpoint 30	Telling the time	64–65
Checkpoint 34	Adding and subtracting money	72–73
Geometry – properties of shapes		
Checkpoint 3	3D shapes	8–9
Checkpoint 14	2D shapes	30–31
Checkpoint 15	Right angles and turns	32–33
Statistics		
Checkpoint 27	Tables, pictograms and bar charts	56–59

*These Checkpoints fall under more than one domain.